JAZZ Technique takes off!

15 intermediate studies
for solo violin and violin duet

MARY COHEN

FABER *ff* MUSIC

© 2009 by Faber Music Ltd
First published in 2009 by Faber Music Ltd
Bloomsbury House 74–77 Great Russell Street London WC1B 3DA
Music processed by Jackie Leigh
Cover illustration by Lynette Williamson
Cover design by Lydia Merrills-Ashcroft
Printed in England by Caligraving Ltd
All rights reserved

ISBN10: 0-571-53263-2
EAN13: 978-0-571-53263-6

To buy Faber Music publications or to find out about the full range of titles available
please contact your local music retailer or Faber Music sales enquiries:
Faber Music Limited, Burnt Mill, Elizabeth Way, Harlow, CM20 2HX England
Tel: +44 (0)1279 82 89 82   Fax: +44 (0)1279 82 89 83
sales@fabermusic.com   fabermusic.com

CONTENTS

Let's do it (let's fall in love)

This is one person trying to convince another that falling in love would be a good idea! Following the dynamics carefully will help to make the 'argument' persuasive. Swing the rhythm in bars 2, 5, 13 and so on. Look for opportunities to use a romantic 'jazzy' vibrato.

Hier versucht eine Person der anderen klarzumachen, wie toll es wäre, sich zu verlieben! Richtig überzeugend wird die Argumentation, wenn du dich genau an die dynamischen Angaben hältst. In den Takten 2, 5, 13 usw. sollte der Rhythmus geswingt werden. Überlege, wo du mit romantischem, „jazzigem" Vibrato spielen kannst.

Words and Music by
Cole Porter

Carnival parade rumba

In this lively rumba, 'think' the pattern of 3+3+2 quavers in your head all the way through, especially in bars with dotted crotchets. To get a real feel for the rhythm, try drumming it first with your fingertips. The accent at the end of each bar helps to keep the energy level high. Make life easy by holding your left-hand fingers down where possible.

Bei diesem lebhaften Rumba muss das Pattern aus 3+3+2 Achteln im Kopf durchlaufen, vor allem in Takten mit punktierten Vierteln. Versuche den Rhythmus erst mit den Fingerspitzen zu klopfen, um ihn ins Gefühl zu bekommen. Der Akzent am Ende jedes Taktes hilft, nicht an Energie zu verlieren. Spare Energie ein, indem du die Finger der linken Hand wo immer möglich unten lässt.

Mary Cohen

I got rhythm Duet

Before you play this duet, have fun vocalising the tune using scat sounds (jazz nonsense syllables). This will get you in the rhythmic mood and help the anticipated notes (bar 6) to feel natural and effortless when you play. For a solo version of the tune, play the top line and swap to the lower line for bars 13–20 and 29–32.

Bevor du dieses Duett spielst, solltest du die Melodie zum Spaß auf Scat-Silben (sinnfreie Silben im Jazz) singen. So kommst du in den Rhythmus und kannst dann die antizipierten Noten (Takt 6) natürlich und mühelos spielen. Für eine Soloversion des Stücks spielst du die obere Stimme und springst nur in den Takten 13–20 und 29–32 in die zweite Stimme.

Music and Lyrics by George Gershwin
and Ira Gershwin

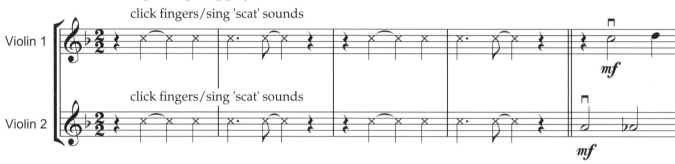

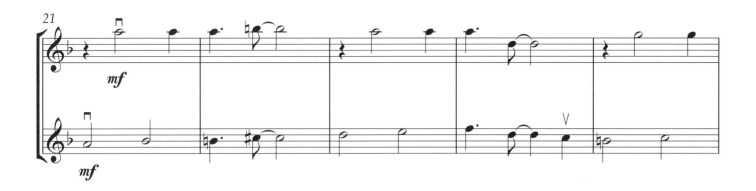

Tattered blue jeans rag

This happy-go-lucky 'blue' rag can be played in first position, but try experimenting with the different sound colours you can make in third position. Start the glissando between bars 7–8 with normal finger pressure, releasing the weight to harmonic pressure as you begin the slide. Use the same finger for the harmonic as for the slide, and lift the finger and bow off the string simultaneously once the harmonic has been reached, so it rings out clearly.

Dieser unbekümmerte „Blue"-Rag kann in der ersten Lage gespielt werden, aber versuche ruhig auch mit den unterschiedlichen Klangfarben der dritten Lage zu experimentieren. Starte das Glissando zwischen T. 7 und 8 mit normalem Fingerdruck, nimm dann im Gleiten Druck weg bis zum Flageolett-Ton. Flageolett und Glissando werden mit dem gleichen Finger gegriffen. Sobald das Flageolett erreicht ist, gehen Finger und Bogen gleichzeitig von der Seite weg, damit der Ton frei klingen kann.

Mary Cohen

Who wants to be a millionaire?

This is a conversation in which one person does most of the talking! The glissando motifs in bars 8 etc. are the second person's slightly bored 'drawl'. Begin the top of the glissando with full finger weight, release to harmonic pressure during the slide, then back to full weight for the final note. See how many different jazz instruments you can mimic in the 'scat' introduction.

Inhalt dieses Stücks ist eine Unterhaltung, die eine Person fast allein bestreitet! Die Glissando-Motive in T. 8 usw. sind die leicht genervten, gedehnten Einwürfe der zweiten Person. Setze beim Glissando mit vollem Fingerdruck an, nimm dann im Gleiten Gewicht weg bis zum Flageolett, dann wieder zurück zum normalen Fingerdruck auf der letzten Note. Versuche in der „Scat"-Einleitung möglichst viele verschiedene Jazzinstrumente nachzuahmen.

Words and Music by Cole Porter

Tuesday, bluesday

Don't let the look of a blues put you off! All the little tied semiquavers are just slight anticipations which moodily push against the beat. The best way to get the feel of a blues rhythm is to sing it, feeling a steady beat in your whole body. The ends of bars 7 and 15 are an insistent 'Yeah, man!' idea.

Keine Angst – die ganzen kleinen gebundenen 16tel sind nur Antizipationen, die leicht gegen den Beat sticheln. Um den Rhythmus eines Blues' ins Gefühl zu bekommen, ist es am besten, ihn erst einmal zu singen und so den durchgehenden Beat im ganzen Körper zu spüren. Den Taktenden von T. 7 & 15 liegt eine wiederkehrende „Yeah, man!"-Idee zugrunde.

Mary Cohen

That dance... that dance...

This is the memory of a slow rumba that seems very special in some way. Play as if your bow is 'breathing' the notes, in the relaxed style of a close-miked jazz singer. Keep the 3+3+2 rhythm at the back of your mind but let the music unfold seamlessly. Experiment with fast, light, portamento finger slides for the highest note where the shifts are marked with a little line. Be careful not to overshoot the F natural in bar 46!

Das Stück erinnert an einen langsamen Rumba, der in gewisser Weise sehr eigen wirkt. Spiele ihn, als würde dein Bogen die Töne entspannt „atmen" wie ein Jazzsänger, der ganz nah am Mikro singt. Der 3+3+2-Rhythmus läuft zwar im Hintergrund durch, die Musik muss sich darüber aber frei entfalten. Experimentiere an den Stellen, wo Lagenwechsel mit einem kleinen Strich markiert sind, mit schnellen, leichten, portamento gespielten Glissandi zur höchsten Note. Vorsicht: Das F in Takt 46 darf dabei nicht zu hoch geraten!

Mary Cohen

A cappuccino at the ice rink

This is a fusion of an elegant waltz and jazz syncopation. Feel the 'one in a bar' pulse and aim for a light, frothy sound! A very relaxed bow-hold will aid the bounce back of the up bows. Watch out for the A♯ at the end of bar 55.

Das Stück ist ein Mix aus elegantem Walzer und Jazz-Synkopen. Spüre den ganztaktigen Puls und achte auf einen leichten und lockeren Klang! Eine sehr entspannte Bogenhaltung hilft beim Springen der Aufstriche.

Mary Cohen

The entertainer Duet

Scott Joplin famously said that ragtime should never be hurried. Think of this as a conversation between two friends who are showing off a little to each other as they take a walk, but always in a good-humoured way. Keep the bow strokes light and stylish.

Scott Joplin sagte bekanntlich, ein Ragtime dürfe nie gehetzt wirken. Stelle dir diesen Ragtime als Unterhaltung zwischen zwei Freunden vor, die nebeneinanderher gehen und vor dem anderen auf nette Art ein klein wenig angeben. Achte auf einen leichten und eleganten Bogenstrich.

Scott Joplin

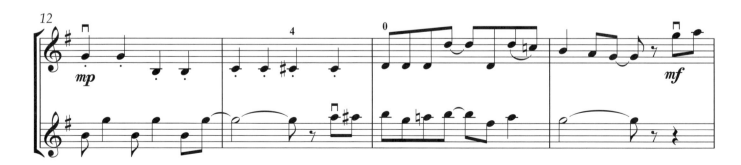

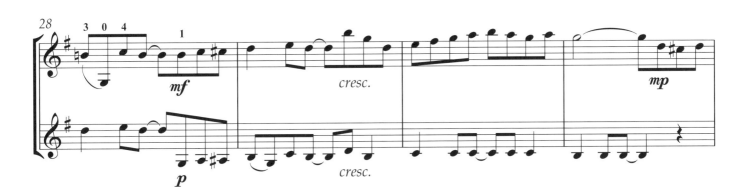

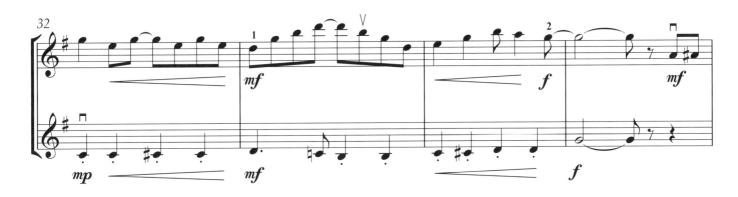

Tango at midnight

The tango is full of sudden twists and turns, stops and starts. A characteristic moment is when the dancer seems to make time stand still for a second; try to capture this feeling between the two up bows in bars 2 and 3, etc. Use strong contrasts in your bow tone: sometimes short, spikey sounds (bars 4 and 6), sometimes a very rich full tone (bars 5, 7, 9, etc.).

Der Tango ist voller plötzlicher Wendungen, Abbrüche und Neuanfänge. Ein typischer Moment ist etwa der, wenn der Tänzer scheinbar die Zeit für eine Sekunde stillstehen lässt. Versuche dieses Gefühl zwischen den zwei Aufstrichen in den Takten 2 und 3 usw. einzufangen. Der Bogenton muss hier sehr kontrastreich sein: kurze, spitze Noten (T. 4 und 6) wechseln ab mit einem sehr vollen, reichen Ton (T. 5, 7, 9 etc.).

Mary Cohen

On the run!

Keep a good octave 'hand-frame' in the position changes throughout this fast-moving piece – but remember to slightly contract it for the higher positions and slightly expand it for the lower ones. Think of this as the background music for a road movie and add dynamics to fit your storyline.

Achte in diesem schnellen Stück darauf, bei den Lagenwechseln einen guten Oktavgriff beizubehalten – aber denke daran, ihn in den oberen Lagen enger und in den unteren etwas weiter zu greifen. Stell dir das Stück als Hintergrundmusik für ein Road Movie vor und ergänze dynamische Angaben, die zu deiner Story passen.

Mary Cohen

Summertime Duet

The tune begins with a light, fast, 'slushy' glissando – look for other places to add this effect. Keep the chromatic accompaniment lazy and unhurried. For an up-bow start at the point, relax your bowhold: soft muscle tissue prevents 'bounce'.

Die Melodie setzt mit einem leichten, schnellen, kitschigen Glissando ein – suche weitere Stellen, wo dieser Effekt passen könnte. Die chromatische Begleitung ist durchgehend träge und gelassen zu spielen. Achte beim Aufstrich an der Spitze auf eine lockere Bogenhaltung: Die Muskulatur muss weich sein, sonst springt der Bogen.

Music and Lyrics by George Gershwin, Du Bose,
Dorothy Heyward and Ira Gershwin

Charleston, let's charleston!

In the 1920s girls shocked the world by going dancing in short, fringed dresses that flapped as they moved. The 'charleston' was a dance with quick, almost jerky movements which was particularly associated with these 'flappers'. In bars 6, 8, 14, etc. use a small amount of bow and little arm movement when crossing the strings; keep a relaxed bowhold and let your fingers control the rhythm and the string crossings.

In den 1920er Jahren schockierten junge Frauen die Welt, indem sie in kurzen, fransigen Kleidern zum Tanzen gingen, die bei jeder Bewegung flatterten. Der 'Charleston', ein Tanz mit schnellen, fast schon ruckartigen Bewegungen, wird eng mit diesen „Flappern" verbunden. Spiele die Saitenübergänge in den Takten 6, 8, 14 usw. mit wenig Bogen und kleinen Armbewegungen; achte auf eine entspannte Bogenhaltung und lass deine Finger Rhythmus und Saitenübergänge kontrollieren.

Mary Cohen

Tip top tap dancer

Tap dancers in 1930s films often seem to play games with the beat – hiding it with slides and syncopations, sometimes followed by sudden stillness. Absolute precision is essential, but the dancer also creates the impression of effortless lightness. Use little bows to keep the tempo under control, and think of the chromatic fingerings as the flashy footwork. Always know exactly where the beat is, especially when it is hidden!

Stepp-Tänzer in Filmen der 1930er Jahren scheinen mit dem Takt oft zu spielen – sie verschleiern ihn durch Rutschbewegungen und Synkopierungen, denen manchmal absolute Stille folgt. Steppen erfordert absolute Perfektion, gleichzeitig aber vermittelt der Tänzer den Eindruck müheloser Leichtigkeit. Spiele mit kurzen Bogenstrichen, um das Tempo zu halten, und stell dir die chromatische Fingertechnik als wirkungsvolle Beinarbeit vor. Du musst immer genau wissen, wo der Takt ist, vor allem da, wo er verschleiert ist.

Mary Cohen

Doin' my head in!

In the second half of the twentieth century some jazz musicians began to play around with changing time signatures. Here, bars of 5/8 and 6/8 alternate in an insistent pattern that is hard to get out of your head! For variety, add your own dynamics and try playing with different bow styles (e.g. sul ponticello, sul tasto, spiccato). You could also put accents in different places to give the rhythm some unexpected twists.

In der zweiten Hälfte des 20. Jahrhunderts begannen einige Jazzmusiker mit Taktwechseln zu spielen. Hier alternieren 5/8- und 6/8-Takt in einem festen Muster, das einem nur schwer aus dem Kopf geht! Ergänze zur Abwechslung deine eigene Dynamik und versuche mit unterschiedlichen Bogentechniken zu spielen (z.B. sul ponticello, sul tasto, spiccato). Du kannst auch an verschiedenen Stellen Akzente setzen und so für rhythmische Überraschungen sorgen.

Mary Cohen

Do-in' my   head in!